The Site Management Safety Training Scheme for the Building and Civil Engineering Industries

Course Notes

XA6

Published by
CITB-ConstructionSkills
Bircham Newton, Kings Lynn,
Norfolk PE31 6RH

First published 1979
Revised 1980
Revised 1983
Revised 1985
Revised 1993
Revised 1995

New edition 1996
Revised 1998
Revised 1999
Revised 2001
Revised 2003

New edition 2007
Revised 2010

Reprinted 2012

The Construction Industry Training Board
otherwise known as CITB-ConstructionSkills and ConstructionSkills is
a registered charity (Charity Number: 264289)

ISBN: 978-1-85751-333-2

Contents

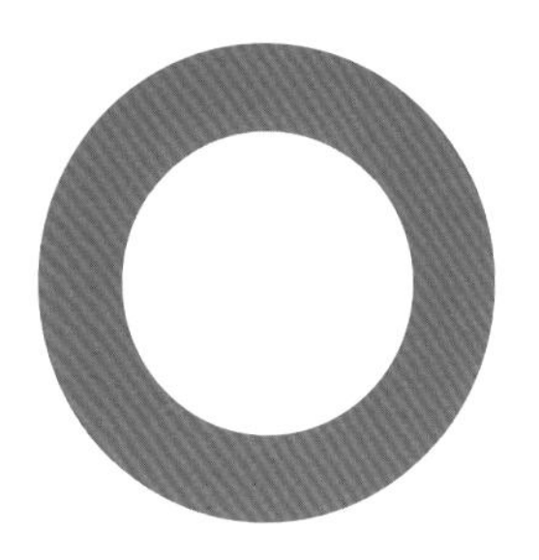

Foreword

Generally, health and safety is managed on construction sites via two approaches:

Physical – risk is reduced through the use of technology and physical means, such as machinery to reduce manual tasks or to make work at height safer, barriers and personal protective equipment.

Managerial – risk is reduced through the application of health and safety management systems that systematically assess construction risk and reduce it to a level that is reasonable. This is achieved through training, information and instruction, together with the production of method statements and safe systems of work that include the selection of appropriate physical means.

There is a growing view within the construction industry that, generally, the best contractors have achieved all the improvements that are possible though the adoption and implementation of only these two approaches to managing risk. However, there is still much to be done to bring all contractors up to the standards of the best.

In the autumn of 2004, six interrelated research reports into construction accidents were published by the Health and Safety Executive (HSE). The following two quotations come from the reports:

"Construction [is] dominated by two cultures: Just get it done, It won't happen to me." [1]

"... in the majority of these [accidents] it was felt that the problem stemmed from a violation of known rules more than a lack of knowledge." [2]

Violating a known rule suggests that risks had been assessed, safe systems of work devised and that training and information, in order to control the residual risk, had been provided. For the construction industry to make the step change required to further improve its health and safety performance, it must start to address the industry's culture and the behaviour of all its individuals. Unless the issue of why safety rules are broken, deliberately changed or ignored is actively addressed, no further significant improvement in health and safety performance will be possible.

In preparation for the Health and Safety Commission's (HSC) Construction Health and Safety Summit, held in February 2005, the Strategic Forum for Construction published its Respect for People (RfP) Code of Good Working Health and Safety Practices. The code requires:

- all contractors to have in place effective management systems that address the RfP agenda to bring about behavioural change
- all construction workers to ensure that they seek to be competent in order to play their full part in improving the attitudes, behaviours and performance of the industry.

---

1 *Research report 231, Improving health and safety in construction, Phase 2 – Depth and breadth, Volume 1 – Summary report*

2 *Research report 233, Improving health and safety in construction, Phase 2 – Depth and breadth, Volume 3 – Construction transport accidents, Underlying causes and risk control*

The award of the Construction Site Manager's Safety Certificate, upon successful completion of this course, shows that employers are committed to the management of health and safety on sites and successful candidates are active in improving their competence. We must all strive to ensure that in exercising the knowledge and skills acquired through this course, certificate holders will be committed to:

- stamping out rule violation
- the improvement of the industry's health and safety performance through the sensible application of risk management techniques.

By all focussing on these issues, we can make the vision of zero accidents on our construction sites a reality.

Introduction to health and safety responsibilities

Introduction

Health and safety law has developed over a long period of time, much of it prompted by industrial disasters (so-called stable door legislation). In recent years it has also been influenced by the United Kingdom being a part of the European Union.

Since the Single European Act was agreed in 1986, the European Commission has issued a range of Directives aimed at producing a common approach to health and safety legislation within the European Union.

In the UK, we have a history of law that spans a number of areas in order to provide protection (health and safety, as well as criminal or penal sanctions) and remedies for breaches of law. The following is a brief outline of the current legal system.

Contract law, common law and statute law

All employers, principal contractors, contractors and the self-employed, as well as employees, can have responsibilities in three distinct areas of law.

Contract law

A contract is an agreement by two parties and requires specific ingredients to ensure it is legally enforceable. A contract implies 'something' going from one party to the other, for example, exchange of goods for payment, services for payment or money for work. Both parties to a contract must intend to make a legally binding contract and have authority to enter into a contract.

Until the Contracts (Rights of Third Parties) Act 1999 the flow was between the two parties to the contract. Under the Act the contract can include or exclude the rights of a third person.

Common law

Common law has evolved over the centuries with judicial judgements creating binding precedents. These are decisions made in higher courts that are binding on all lower courts. For example, a decision made by the House of Lords is binding on all lower courts.

These judicial precedents are presented in the form of case law, for example, Wilsons and Clyde Coal Co. Ltd. versus English (1938); which in this case identified the common law duties of an employer to his employees.

At common law, an individual has the right to protection from harm and the right to sue for compensation, when they suffer loss or ill health or injury through the negligence of another.

Statute law

Statute law comprises Acts of Parliament, Regulations and EU Directives.

Acts of Parliament are laws made by the government of the day. For example, The Health and Safety at Work etc Act 1974, is an enabling act. An enabling act, in this case, is one that permits the Secretary of State or other Ministers to replace piecemeal legislation with regulations requiring a higher standard of health, safety and welfare.

The regulations are referred to as statutory instruments. They are made under an enabling act, for example, The Noise at Work Regulations 2006 or as a result of a European Directive, for example, The Manual Handling Operations Regulations 1992.

The contents of EU Directives have to be incorporated within our legislation within a specified timescale.

Modern health and safety management recognises three important issues:

a) the commitment of senior level management within a company to promoting and recognising a safe working environment (for example, reporting on health and safety activities in the shareholder's or annual report)

b) the responsibility of managers at all levels for developing and maintaining effective control systems

c) the need for all employees to develop their own critical health and safety attitude to the workplace.

In fact, total quality must include the ultimate goal for health and safety – a working environment free from potential harm, injury or health hazards.

The emphasis is on the setting up and running of effective systems – not on clearing up after the event.

Duties and responsibilities for health, safety and welfare

Employers' responsibilities

The Health and Safety at Work etc Act 1974 places general duties on employers to ensure, so far as is reasonably practicable, the health, safety and welfare at work of all their employees, and of any others not employed by them who might be affected by the operations they control.

This includes the requirement for a safe place of work. The Management of Health and Safety at Work Regulations 1999 requires risk assessments to be undertaken so that preventative and protective steps can be identified to control hazards in the workplace.

Construction site managers, as their employers' representatives, now need to become familiar with the principles of the two regulations that make those general requirements more specific.

i) **The Management of Health and Safety at Work Regulations 1999** (The Management Regulations). The Approved Code of Practice (ACoP) gives managers a detailed interpretation of these provisions.

ii) **The Construction (Design and Management) Regulations (CDM) 2007** and their ACoP are intended to draw attention to both The Management Regulations and The Provision and Use of Work Equipment Regulations (PUWER) 1998 for the building and civil engineering industry.

Other sets of regulations that have come into force over recent years are covered in Construction Site Safety ***(GE 700)***

The Workplace (Health, Safety and Welfare) Regulations 1992

The Workplace (Health, Safety and Welfare) Regulations do not generally apply to construction sites, or to building and construction work within a workplace if it is fenced off. However, they do apply to the building under construction, once completed, and to the welfare arrangements on site. The relevant Approved Code of Practice (HSE publication L24 Workplace health, safety and welfare, Approved Code of Practice and guidance) contains valuable and often detailed practical advice on a range of matters related to the work environment. Managers will find it extremely useful when seeking suitable guidelines in this area.

Persons with specific duties and responsibilities for health and safety on site need a sound understanding of the principles of all the relevant statutory legislation. The regulations, and particularly their ACoPs, help to focus the attention of managers on the special hazards and safety measures required in particular situations in the construction industry. It is self-evident that understanding the principles of the legislation and complying with it must make a significant contribution to improving health and safety at work.

For further information, see Construction Site Safety ***(GE 700)****, Chapter A01 Health and safety law*

The Management of Health and Safety at Work Regulations 1999

The Management of Health and Safety at Work Regulations (The Management Regulations) overlap with existing more specific regulations, such as The Control of Substances Hazardous to Health Regulations (COSHH) 2002 (as amended). Where regulations do overlap, the latter would normally be sufficient to comply with the corresponding duty imposed by The Management Regulations. However, where duties, under these regulations, go further than the existing specific regulations, additional measures would be needed in order to comply.

Where applicable, employers with five or more employees are required to record their various arrangements for health and safety. Such records could form part of the employer's health and safety policy documentation and arrangements for its implementation.

*For further information, see Construction Site Safety **(GE 700)**, Chapter A01 Health and safety law*

Modification concerning safety representatives. The Safety Representatives and Safety Committees Regulations 1977 were modified by an addition to The Management Regulations, relating to the employer's duty to consult and provide facilities and assistance. In addition, the employer is required to consult with safety representatives in adequate time, prior to any implementation in working or material changes.

*For further information, see Construction Site Safety **(GE 700)**, Chapter A09 Leadership and worker engagement*

The Health and Safety (Consultation with Employees) Regulations 1996 were introduced because The Health and Safety at Work Act only covered union-appointed safety representatives, and their rights of consultation with employers. These rights now extend to all employees and give everyone, whether union-appointed or not, the right to have consultation with their employers and to be provided with information.

There are many similarities with The Safety Representative and Safety Committee Regulations and they also implement the 'consultation' provisions of the European Union Framework Directive on health and safety.

Employers must also provide safety representatives with the facilities and assistance they reasonably require to carry out their functions under The Health and Safety at Work Act and The Management Regulations.

The Construction (Design and Management) Regulations (CDM) 2007

The principal aim of these regulations is to raise the standard of health and safety in the building and construction industry. This is to be achieved by improving co-ordination between the various parties involved at the preparation stage of a construction project, and also while work is being carried out.

The Management Regulations and The Provision and Use of Work Equipment Regulations (PUWER) 1998 are supplemented by these regulations. All the 1960s Construction Regulations were repealed and only The Construction (Head Protection) Regulations 1989 remain in force, along with The Work at Height Regulations (WAHR) 2005.

The general principles of prevention and protection, outlined by the guidance to The CDM Regulations, must be applied by all those persons responsible for deciding the measures to be taken following risk assessments, and by those responsible under The CDM Regulations when they take decisions affecting health and safety during the project.

The health and safety decisions made will naturally reflect the tremendous diversity of all the factors at play in the building and civil engineering industry. At certain stages of a project, some of these principles may have greater impact than others. However, all such decisions must still be based on the careful application of the complete package of principles.

*For further information, see Construction Site Safety **(GE 700)**, Chapter A03 Construction (Design and Management) Regulations*

Managing health and safety at work

Obligation to achieve safety

There are strong social, moral, legal and economic reasons for preventing accidents and risks to health. As individuals, we all have social and legal responsibilities to avoid taking actions that endanger the health and safety of others. As employers or employees, we have social and legal responsibilities and there are also economic reasons to ensure safe and healthy working conditions.

Economic costs

It is estimated that accidents and ill health cost the construction industry a sum in excess of £4,000 million each year due to lost production, wages paid but not earned, disruption of work plans, damage to materials and plant, etc. The figure does not include insurance premiums and compensation awards. Families and individuals are also likely to lose both physically and financially. No one makes a profit – no one wants an accident.

Reference
*HSE publication **INDG 355** Reduce risks – cut costs*
The real costs of accidents and ill health at work

Human costs

In human terms the construction industry loses 4 million working days a year due to accidents and ill health, causing misery to individuals and their families and friends. At work, morale and motivation can drop drastically on sites where a serious accident has occurred, or where the employer and management have not taken clear and obvious steps to create safe and healthy working conditions.

Reference
www.hse.gov.uk/statistics/industry/construction
LFS and SWI surveys
*HSE publication **HSG48** Reducing error and influencing behaviour*

Legal sanctions

The Health and Safety at Work Act details the range of sanctions and punitive legal actions that can be taken against employers who do not carry out their statutory duties.

Reference
*Construction Site Safety **(GE 700)**,*
Chapter A02 The Health and Safety at Work Act

Safety and efficiency

Safety and health at work, and efficient working practices, are not mutually exclusive concepts. It is easy to foresee numerous instances where safety and economic efficiency go together, or where good industrial relations and the reputation of a company can be put at risk by poor management decisions concerning safety and health. A serious accident may easily cause any of the following: loss of output; damage to plant and materials; a legal penalty being imposed and an industrial dispute taking place.

Health and safety do not stand alone. By adopting a positive approach to accident prevention, site managers can help to ensure that a site will be safe, productive and have good labour relations. On a well-managed site, work is usually on schedule, within budget and without accidents or ill health.

Health and safety policy

The successful implementation of health and safety policy and arrangements in any organisation relies on its management skill and the application of the following elements:

- a high degree of management commitment
- an effective means of communication within the organisation
- the motivation of employees
- the management's awareness of their authority, and of the extent of their responsibility
- planning skills
- the effective co-ordination of work
- the effective monitoring and controlling of health and safety procedures
- quality of decision making
- the provision of proper resources for health and safety.

The health and safety policy has little value unless it is effectively communicated to all employees within the organisation. Training is one method of conveying substantial or complex information. In this section we concentrate on the content, availability, purposes and means of communicating the most important health and safety information.

Reference
*Construction Site Safety **(GE 700)***
Chapter A02 The Health and Safety at Work Act
Chapter A04 Health and safety policies
Chapter A05 Risk assessments and method statements

Effective communication

Regardless of the specific area of responsibility, the manager is at the heart of a complex network of communication that contains a challenging variety of messages, channels, purposes and people. Getting the best results from communication is nowhere more vital than in the field of health and safety.

Effective communication – a simple model

Managers who want an in-depth coverage of communication theories and techniques are recommended to consult any of the numerous textbooks and manuals readily available on business communication. For the purposes of this section, a basic model will help us to identify the significant elements in effective communication. Harold Lasswell (1948) set up this simple questioning device.

> *'The likelihood of your communication being effective should be enhanced by answering this five-point question:*
>
> **Who** says **what** in which **channel** to **whom** with what **effect**?'

The question recognises that people are involved in an interactive relationship, and that each message has a purpose. That means we have to make choices about the most suitable means for conveying it.

If we assume that 'effect' includes the important idea of feedback, it is useful to add one more question, i.e. 'in what context' is the communication taking place?

The context and the relationships may well contain potential barriers to communication. Allowing for these, as we must, the communication promises to be effective if each stage of the question is answered fully and accurately.

Communication

Communication is essential, particularly for the health and safety policy to be known, understood, accepted and implemented by employees at every level in the organisation. The best policy in the world and the most detailed procedures will be useless if they are not communicated effectively to everyone concerned.

Working situations differ greatly between organisations in the industry. Managers should review the various means of communication available to them and choose the most appropriate for the topic and the audience.

The need for a system of communication will depend on the size of the organisation. The larger the organisation, the greater the distance between the parties involved and, in turn, the greater is the need for dealing with communication systematically and effectively.

Whatever the size or the extent of communication systems in the organisation, managers must decide the following:

- the precise information they, their colleagues and their subordinates need
- when they need it
- how it should be made available.

Above all, they must recognise that the communication process has succeeded only if the provider of the information knows that it has been both received and understood. The language used and the means chosen to convey the message both contribute to the success of the process.

In addition, the manager must check that the information or instructions have been understood and are being observed. Putting the health and safety statement on a canteen notice-board, and then forgetting all about it, is not effective communication.

Three communication methods

Organisations which operate an effective health and safety policy use three methods. The size and nature of the organisation's work will determine how much use is made of each method, but they will all make a significant contribution. The methods are:

- face-to-face discussion
- visible behaviour, 'leading by example'
- written communication.

Face-to-face

This method in particular allows for the exchange of ideas and individual participation, thereby supporting and amplifying the other communication methods used.

Here are examples of some of the opportunities for face-to-face discussion on health and safety matters:

- an individual conversation between managers and their subordinates
- the meetings of a trade union branch and safety committees
- small group briefings to pass on new information
- the inclusion of health and safety on the agenda of all routine meetings between managers and supervisors
- the internal or external training provisions
- talks by experts on specific subjects.

Guidelines for effective spoken communication

These guidelines can apply to face-to-face or telephone contacts, coaching or training situations, briefing small groups and contributing to meetings.

Spoken communication is direct. It allows for instant feedback and for everyone present to get involved. It often needs to be supplemented by written confirmation to ensure a shared understanding of what took place and what was discussed.

- **Compose the message carefully** and think about who you are talking to, the precise information you need to convey, and the action or response you want from them. Organise the information in a logical order.
- **Convey the information clearly** by using language, including body language and tone of voice, that suits both your purpose and the situation. Jargon works well in its place, but your listeners must know what it means.
- **Put yourself in their position** to make sure they are capable of understanding what you are saying. Make special provision for those with hearing or comprehension difficulties, or for those whose first language is not English.
- **Use non-verbal means** such as plans, drawings and symbols to help convey information. If your communication is long or complex, make use of suitable pauses. Check that understanding is taking place.

- **Use a direct style** remembering that repetition is useful for emphasis or reinforcement but not for its own sake. Avoid indirect or subtle features like sarcasm, innuendo, ambiguity or vagueness. They generally result in misunderstanding.
- **Check for feedback** because you need to know that your message has been received, accepted and understood. Your listeners' responses may indicate attitudes or opinions that lead you towards further or modified action.
- **Follow-up** because, after the event, you still need to know that the content of your communication has been acted upon, or continues to be put into effect. This stage can be delegated to another manager or supervisor, or it may require your personal attention.

Visible behaviour

Supervisors and managers at all levels can demonstrate their commitment to health and safety by consistent behaviour which is seen to be genuine. We will all learn from example if we respect those providing it, and believe that they are sincere. In addition to scrupulous observation of essential practices, the following activities will act as reinforcement:

- regular tours of work areas (not inspections) by managers, where observation and discussion of health and safety issues is the central objective
- active participation on health and safety committees
- supportive involvement in investigations into accidents and ill health issues when they arise.

Written communication

This should include the health and safety policy statement itself, as well as documents outlining the health and safety responsibilities, performance standards, procedures for risk control and quite specific instructions for particular jobs or situations.

Generally speaking, the greater the risk, the more specific the instructions need to be. The form of written communication must reflect the needs and abilities of those at the receiving end.

Notices, posters, leaflets and newsletters are other forms of written communication used, depending on the purpose and local working conditions. These are particularly useful for reminding employees of existing regulations, to provide updating and convey progress reports or the results of investigations.

Guidelines for effective written communication

Letters, memos, reports, minutes and notices all take time to produce and can cause problems of misunderstanding if they are not suitably worded. They put a distance between those involved and do not allow for prompt feedback.

However, they do provide a permanent record and are generally the better media for conveying complex or analytical material. By using a written communication, you can reach a large number of recipients and can generally confirm or clarify a previously spoken message.

Assuming a proficient level of writing skills, here are some additional guidelines for effective written communication:

- **draft the material first** to ensure that all points are included, and are in a logical order. The communication should have a brief summarising heading, a clear introduction, development, and conclusion
- **the final paragraph** should state the response information or action you require and a precise deadline date. Mention how and when you can be contacted if further information or discussion is needed
- **keep it simple** by using headings, sub-headings and numbering to identify individual points. Write in short sentences and short paragraphs, using the minimum words needed to convey your message clearly
- **use jargon only** when you are sure the reader will understand it. Avoid unusual vocabulary, and convert the very formal language found in legislation and regulations into language your reader will understand
- **write to the right people** and, if possible, name everyone you intend to receive the communication, including those being copied for information only. Include your own name as the originator
- **use enclosures** to send additional documents, drawings or very complicated material. If you try to include them in the body of a letter or report, they may obscure what you are trying to say
- **feedback and follow-up** as you may need to chase the recipients for action by further written, or spoken, communication. Remember that the purpose of your communication has not been achieved until you know that the action it asks for has been taken.

As a receiver of communications

- You must concentrate on what you are reading or listening to
- You must provide feedback where you can to assist the communication process
- You should request clarification if you don't understand something you are being told
- You should think about the implications of the message before you take any action, or pass on the contents to anyone else
- You must be alert to hidden messages and learn to read between the lines
- You should be sure that your response or action is exactly what is required.

Motivation

Motivation at work is the force that keeps us going and drives us to complete what we are doing. Financial incentives can contribute to this, but we are also motivated by the satisfaction we derive from our work and by the way we are regarded by our fellow employees. The presence of hazardous conditions, or an awareness that management does not take our health and safety seriously, can reduce our motivation to do certain kinds of work.

In general, it is the manager's responsibility to motivate employees to work consistently and effectively. This must include concern for the health and safety of all – ourselves, colleagues and all who may be affected by our undertakings.

We all value our own physical and mental well-being. The manager has to ensure that each employee knows how to protect and guarantee that well-being in the context of their job.

If we accept that everyone in the organisation has a responsibility for health and safety, then the manager's role in the motivation should be to develop co-operation and participation at, and between all levels of management and workers.

Managers and supervisors can achieve this in several ways by:

- creating a working environment where everyone in the organisation understands that we all benefit from good health and safety practice
- actively encouraging and supporting appointed persons and safety representatives, involving them in planning and the reviewing of performance
- including employees in the problem-solving process arising from specific incidents
- operating suggestion schemes, and generally encouraging open communication on health and safety issues.

Even if such open communication generates disagreement over what may be defined as safe working, the process itself should reinforce co-operation and enhance motivation if handled by managers and supervisors in a sensitive and constructive way.

Authority and responsibility

In an organisation that is developing a safe and healthy working culture, every employee has some responsibility for health and safety. This obligation is contained in The Health and Safety at Work Act.

Individual managers and supervisors will also have specific, identified duties and responsibilities within the area they control, enabling decisions to be made and actions taken promptly in emergencies.

It is essential that the manager's authority and responsibilities are precisely documented in their written job description. Duties and functions should be listed in detail, and the limits of their authority made absolutely clear.

In order for the safe working culture to develop properly, it also becomes important for all those with identified health and safety functions to know the responsibilities and authority limits of their colleagues and superiors, as well as their own.

Limits of authority must be clearly understood, particularly in the case of specialist advisers. If the role of such advisers or consultants is solely to advise managers on health and safety, they will have no executive powers whatsoever. Their relationships function only through the correct lines of communication and not through lines of command or responsibility.

A clear understanding of health and safety responsibilities is also very important where several organisations are working together. In the building and construction industry this applies especially to the relationship between principal contractors and contractors.

Managers' responsibilities

The elements that contribute both to the general prosperity of an organisation and to the successful implementation of its health and safety policy are set out below. They apply in all organisations, regardless of size or the nature of the work involved:

- management commitment
- effective communication within the organisation
- the motivation of employees
- the managers' awareness of their authority, and of the extent of their responsibility
- planning skills
- effective co-ordination of work
- effective monitoring and controlling of health and safety procedures
- the quality of decision making
- the provision of proper resources for health and safety.

These points need to be considered by managers and supervisors in two ways:

- to assess their own abilities as managers or supervisors, and
- to relate them to their own specific work situation.

Supervisors

Line managers and supervisors with specified health and safety duties have general responsibility in three key areas:

- in developing the health and safety policy laid down in the first instance by management
- in relating health and safety activities to the legal requirements, to minimise all risks
- in implementing health and safety plans and reporting on their effectiveness.

Successful achievement in those key areas depends on managers and supervisors establishing and maintaining control.

The central themes are open communication and co-operation. These elements are indispensable for the effective development and exercise of control functions by line managers.

Contractors

Effective health and safety provision depends on co-operation and communication between all those parties responsible for it. Contractors are frequently employers in their own right, and The Health and Safety at Work Act requires an employer to ensure, as far as is reasonably practicable, that nobody is exposed to health and safety risks from their undertaking; this includes employees, visitors, members of the public and children.

These duties are additional to those towards employees detailed in the Act, and mean that both principal contractors and contractors have a duty of care towards each other's employees, and towards anyone else who might be affected. The Act also extends these duties in respect of the self-employed.

In brief, all employers have responsibilities to see that their work does not compromise the health and safety of themselves, of their employees, or of any other person.

Contractors should be invited to participate, wherever possible, in all stages of the health and safety plan for the site or project, from the formation to the implementation and review. It is advisable to treat the self-employed and labour-only contractor as direct employees for health and safety purposes, unless they can demonstrate that they have made proper and adequate health and safety arrangements.

Labour-only contractors present a special case: the employees of a labour-only contractor, or a self-employed individual, should be placed under the control of one of the principal contractor's supervisors.

Non-employees

Persons in control of any non-domestic premises must ensure, so far as is reasonably practicable, that people using their premises as a place of work are protected from any health and safety risks arising from the use of the premises, their access to it, their egress from it, and from any work activities carried out there. This is a requirement of The Health and Safety at Work Act, and reasserts the concept of health and safety being everybody's concern.

The person in control of the premises is defined as one who has, through contract or tenancy, an obligation of any extent relating to the maintenance or repair of the premises, or the means of access, or guarding against hazards from the plant or substances there.

This potentially large number of people presents difficulties for effective control. The emphasis here is on the provision of relevant health and safety information, as the responsible person may have little or no influence over the movements or actions of the non-employees.

However, if the premises comply fully with the legal duties of its prescribed use, it should be fundamentally safe for non-employees already. There should be relatively few, if any, additional precautions or warnings for non-employees, which should compensate for their unfamiliarity with the premises and work going on there.

Manufacturers, designers and suppliers

The Health and Safety at Work Act, as amended by the Consumer Protection Act 1987, requires those who manufacture, design or supply articles or substances for use by persons at work to ensure that they are safe and without risk to health at all times when being prepared for use, used, cleaned or maintained, by a person at work.

They must also provide all the information necessary to enable their products to be used or maintained safely. This may be particularly important when making an assessment under COSHH.

Similar provisions apply to those who erect or install any article for use by persons at work. The health and safety of anyone using and maintaining the article must not be endangered by the way it was erected or installed.

Health and safety planning skills

Effective planning for health and safety is concerned with the prevention of accidents and ill health, through identifying, eliminating and controlling hazards and risks.

Health and safety management is inseparable from quality management. Similarly, health and safety planning has to be seen as an integral part of operational planning.

Every operational decision has a potential health and safety implication. If it is decided that a particular hazardous material should be delivered on site during a particular week, arrangements must be made for it to be received and handled safely, and to be stored in suitable conditions. In addition to this, those who will use it must be told of its dangers and methods of safe use.

If we accept that prevention is the key theme of a positive health and safety policy, then it is clear that health and safety planning must become part of the overall planning at the earliest possible stage.

Health and safety planning is ideally undertaken by a team of people, contributing their knowledge and experience. Those nearest the job, and so nearest to the hazard, can frequently make the most useful contributions from their everyday experience.

Planning choices are made about issues such as these:

- the size of the workforce
- the most suitable plant, machinery, equipment and materials for the job to be carried out safely
- the correct timing and sequencing of operations
- movements of both vehicles and material
- safe working methods.

The main considerations are usually those of efficiency and cost. In the well-managed safety culture, health and safety considerations need to play an equal part in the making of those operational choices.

No single manager is expected to foresee all the potential risks and hazards. This makes a strong case for small groups of employees with particular expertise to concentrate on the risks related to their specialism. This more detailed health and safety planning will make extra demands on the manager's skills in communication and organisation.

The effective incorporation of health and safety into the planning of on-site operations clearly becomes a team activity. The work of one section may have implications for the safety of those working on the neighbouring section. For example, drivers will be concerned for the safety of themselves and their vehicles as well as anyone who happens to be walking across the site.

The team activity required for health and safety planning is a reminder of the importance of open and effective channels of communication. This is the essential condition for co-operation. In its turn, that co-operation demands planning and organising.

The interrelated nature of the on-site experience, involving physical and human resources, cannot be overemphasised. Full appreciation of this lies at the heart of the well-managed health and safety working culture.

Planning is the essential key to ensuring that health and safety efforts work. Planning for health and safety includes setting standards which help to build a positive culture and which should identify who does what, when and with whom and with what result. The five key points about standards, is that they must be SMART, for example:

Specific
Measurable
Achievable
Realistic
Time-related

Effective co-ordination of work

Control is a management function, and co-ordination of activities is a tool of control. Once the operational plan has started to become a reality on site, the manager's co-ordinating role should ensure that work activities:

- happen at the right place
- happen at the right time
- happen in the correct sequence

and that they are performed by trained and competent people:

- with the correct materials and equipment
- to agreed quality standards
- within the agreed time-scale
- with the appropriate concern for health and safety implications.

Just as planning demands the fullest possible co-operation and team participation, successful co-ordination of operations at any level depends on properly functioning communication.

Work co-ordination, with the proper incorporation of health and safety activities, is a continuous process. The effective manager or supervisor will need to consider the effects of:

- plant breakdown or
- requirements to speed up the construction process, because of events happening elsewhere on the project
- whether the job is being done at the right time, at the right place, etc.

The manager or supervisor should also be questioning whether a job is physically possible and whether any changes can still be accommodated, without prejudicing the health and safety standards required to ensure compliance with statutory requirements, and the organisation's own health and safety standards.

Effective monitoring and control of health and safety procedures

The heading above can usefully be reduced to two words – **measuring performance**. A low accident rate, even over a long period, may only be the result of chance. On their own, low accident rates are no guarantee of the effective control of risks. If we have planned for health and safety, we must measure actual performance against the standards set in the plan.

Monitoring is a continuous process of observation and inspection of work activities in progress. Controlling is the comparison made between actual and planned performance. Together, they are used to measure performance, and this should be a line manager's responsibility.

For effective health and safety, we need two monitoring approaches, based on the before-and-after model:

- **proactive monitoring** measures health and safety in the preventive area and checks compliance with standards and planned objectives for safe and healthy working, before any accidents have happened
- **reactive monitoring** looks at accidents and incidents themselves, how they occurred and how they were reported and investigated.

Where a discrepancy is identified, both forms of monitoring should follow this system of response:

1. assess the action required to deal with any immediate risks
2. assess the level and type of investigation required
3. carry out an investigation
4. report and analyse the findings of that investigation
5. review all relevant health and safety provisions, including the monitoring systems themselves.

Note:

a) Since reactive monitoring responds to an actual event, some first aid type of response may be necessary before the whole response procedure is started.

b) Similarly, at step 1 above, some immediate action may be needed to eliminate further damage or risk.

Monitoring, including auditing schemes, is covered in more detail in Section 4 and Construction Site Safety ***(GE 700)****, Chapter A10 Inspections and audits*

Quality of decision making

In management training, decision making is often paired, even confused, with problem solving. In this section, we are not looking at problem solving, which we can define as a state of disorder capable of solution. Problems in the construction process are solved every day at an operational level. They include rapid-response solutions to health and safety problems. If the necessary information is available, and we can predict the outcome accurately, we can take action and eliminate the problem.

The management decisions which really matter are strategic. They concern long-term aspects of the organisation's development. They frequently involve efficient use of resources to meet policy objectives. This is as true of health and safety decision making as of other areas of management responsibility.

Before embarking on a decision-making process, we must ask 'Is a decision really necessary?' The answer is that it is necessary when a condition is likely to worsen, or if an important opportunity for improvement is likely to be missed. Experienced managers recognise that most situations fall somewhere between the two.

The following procedure enables managers to make the best use of their time:

1. define the problem
2. analyse the problem
3. develop alternative solutions
4. decide on the best solution
5. execute (implement) the decision
6. receive feedback.

Provision of proper resources for health and safety

The organisation which has provided effective health and safety management can recognise that failure in this area represents unnecessary loss. Costs can be reduced by minimising risks to physical and human resources.

Some resources are abstract, such as a commitment to health and safety. However, we have now seen how a commitment can be made to a positive health and safety working culture. Everything discussed so far has cost implications, from planning for health and safety to the monitoring of implemented systems.

At the operational level, physical safety resources will be required, such as machine guards, personal protective equipment and special storage for hazardous substances. The cost of such provisions has to be added to the costs of setting up, maintaining and reviewing the health and safety procedures, and the methods of working they demand.

Recurring training needs will become apparent with staff turnover; changing methods of work, equipment and materials; and with alterations to building regulations and other legislation. This is a key cost or resource implication.

Managers share with everyone else the responsibility for health and safety on the site. Managers with specific health and safety duties and responsibilities must recognise and calculate the resources they will need to exercise those responsibilities. They must also ensure that the resources are made available.

The ready availability of resources for health and safety will develop as the safe working culture develops within the organisation, through open communication and co-operation.

Reference
*HSE publication **INDG 355** Reduce risks – cut costs*
The real costs of accidents and ill health at work
HSE publication Reducing risks, protecting people
(only available at: www.hse.gov.uk/risk/theory/r2p2.pdf)

Summary – Safety management programme

Elements in the cycle

The preceding section can be summed up by the use of the following steps or elements in a management cycle. The three key elements are:

- policy development
- development of organisation
- development of techniques of planning, measuring and reviewing.

Policy development must:

- contribute to business performance as well as meeting health and safety requirements
- link with the principles of risk management
- have a positive impact on all activities.

Organisation:

- must translate policy into practice
- requires visible and active management
- requires a positive and supportive safety culture
- requires motivation and involvement of competent people
- must demand active participation of workforce
- must implement consultation with workforce.

Planning and risk assessment involves:

- quantifying risks and prioritising actions
- establishing standards
- reviewing risk management strategies.

Implementation:

- requires sound management, standard operating procedures and performance criteria
- requires communications more obvious by their quality than their absence.

Measuring performance:

- must be measured against predetermined standards
- must relate to hardware, software and human factors (individual performance)
- must use many different sources of data
- must receive feedback of information, against standards, forming a basis of self-regulation and an opportunity to reward good performance.

Responsibilities of managers and supervisors

Managers and supervisors are required to exercise their particular skills to ensure a high standard of health and safety performance within their organisations.

Control procedures

Control procedures on construction sites are needed because of the complexity of the operational processes and the range of legislation affecting their conduct. The larger the organisation, the greater the need for a systems approach, that is, for procedures and the means of communicating them to all concerned to be in place.

In general terms, the health and safety policy is implemented through a variety of procedures, both formal and informal, as detailed below. The details of the organisation's health and safety policy will contain, *at least*, the safety standards required by law. 'At least' is emphasised because, in a well-managed health and safety environment, the legal requirements should be seen as the minimum starting point for a safety policy.

A system of communications has to be set up to ensure the universal awareness, understanding, acceptance and implementation of the safety that is required. Agreements between employers and trade unions, at local or national level, can contain specific procedures. They may refer to actual working practices or, for example, to the reporting of company policies or incidents themselves.

Informal procedures may be put in place by an individual (supervisor or manager), if these have been first agreed with management. These may reflect the individual's experience of particular situations or operations; or their preferred method of organising the work of their team; or of a temporary state of affairs that applies in a limited and local way.

These procedures will generally take place at a specific and detailed level that would only receive very broad treatment in the organisation's health and safety policy document. They tend to occur in these areas:

- short-term planning for a one-off or temporary situation
- progress reporting
- safety and quality inspections
- processes not covered by standard procedures.

Supervision and task management

Whatever the procedure may be, it will operate through two central aspects of supervision: task management and team building.

Task management

Effective task management aims to achieve the organisation's specific health and safety objectives. This requires the necessary steps to ensure proper understanding of risks and performance standards, and the effective and consistent operation of procedures.

It also involves:

- planning to achieve very specific objectives at a local level
- the recognition of training needs of individuals
- regular monitoring of existing standards or procedures, which may need modifying in the light of experience, or changed circumstances.

Supervision and team building

The managers' and supervisors' role in securing co-operation, along with working together to achieve health and safety objectives, brings us back to open communication.

Positive team attitudes and approaches will be developed by:

- leading team briefings, problem-solving activity and information sessions
- encouraging individuals to adopt a more active team approach
- developing an awareness of risks affecting the individual as well as the whole group, and of the means to eliminate or control them better.

The level of such supervision depends on two factors: the **risks** involved and the **competence** of individual employees to recognise them and act accordingly.

Supervisors and managers should make special provisions for new employees and trainees, as well as for new or special risk situations.

Alternative methods of team working

Many organisations are developing alternative team-working methods, such as multi-skilling. Among their aims are the possibilities offered by flexible working, and extending the job content. This can have the following effects:

1. Some demarcation lines may disappear, causing mixed work groups of, for example, maintenance and production workers.
2. Individual employees may need to acquire new skills to handle a new task and therefore face new risks.
3. Supervisors and managers may become responsible for new areas of work with additional health and safety objectives.

Managers and supervisors, affected by the above, must not implement new initiatives without first considering the health and safety implications.

Suitable training must be provided before any manager or supervisor can undertake the responsibilities described above.

Job description and health and safety

Authority and responsibility for health and safety should be precisely documented in the written job description of any manager and supervisor, and be focused on meeting performance standards.

Difficulties have arisen in the past over definitions of employer, employee and the self-employed person, and their duties and responsibilities for health and safety on site.

The Health and Safety at Work Act and other current legislation removes such difficulties, in that the employer, or overall controller of the site, also has clear health and safety duties to people other than direct employees. This is extended to members of the public near the site who may be affected by, for example, harmful emissions or falling objects.

In plain terms, everyone on site has a responsibility for health and safety. Managers and supervisors will have specified duties. However, in developing a positive health and safety culture on site, it is important for all job descriptions to draw attention to each employee's personal duty in this area.

On site, health and safety is everybody's business

Job description example

The following is an example of the job description for a manager, for example, site agent or site manager. In setting out the main health and safety responsibilities and duties, it gives an insight into the considerable range and variety of those commitments; and into the extent of the performance measurements to be undertaken by their superior.

- Organise the site so that work is carried out to company standards, and without risk of injury to employees, visitors or others, or damage to equipment or materials.
- Issue work method instructions, or job safety instructions, preferably in written form.
- Know the principles of relevant health and safety legislation, approved codes of practice and official guidance.
- Know and implement the company health and safety policy.
- Ensure that all statutory requirements are complied with on site, and that all registers, records and reports are correctly maintained; that the appointed 'competent person' has sufficient knowledge and experience to carry out the duties imposed on them.
- Give all supervisors, trades supervisors and gangers precise instructions on their responsibilities for correct and safe working methods. Ensure that they do not permit employees, apprentices or trainees to take risks or indulge in any unsafe practices.
- Arrange the delivery, storage and stacking of materials in order to avoid any unnecessary risks.
- Position plant and machinery so that it is safe, and ensure that the electricity supply and all electrical equipment is installed and maintained without risk to persons or equipment.
- Plan and maintain a safe and tidy site.
- Implement safety arrangements with contractors so as to avoid any possibility of confusion about areas of safety responsibility.
- Check that all machinery, plant and tools (including hand tools), are maintained in good condition.
- Ensure that the appropriate protective clothing and equipment are available on site and used when necessary.
- Ensure that the requirements of The Health and Safety (First Aid) Regulations 1981 are complied with, especially regarding qualified first aiders and the provision of first-aid equipment.

- In the event of an accident, see that proper care is taken of casualties, and also know where to obtain further medical assistance if necessary.
- Co-operate fully with the safety adviser, make arrangements to accompany them on their inspections when possible and always act upon any recommendations made.
- Accompany the Health and Safety Executive Inspector, or Environmental Health Officers, on site visits and implement their recommendations as soon as practicable.
- Release supervisors and operatives, when necessary, for on-site or off-site training.
- Liaise with the local fire authority on fire prevention.
- Set a good personal example with regards to health and safety.
- Nominate another person on site to act in your absence or in an emergency.
- Liaise with the appointed person(s) nominated to assist in undertaking health and safety measures.

Informal arrangements

As part of the larger control structure in an organisation, informal arrangements can often constitute a flexible response to circumstances at a very localised level. They may satisfy an immediate or short-term need and are frequently perfectly effective, being of benefit to all concerned.

However, the fact that such arrangements are informal, and probably communicated among the work team by word of mouth, can cause difficulty in the event of dispute. Responsibility can be evaded, and the quality of supervision undermined.

Effective control at higher levels is also threatened if managers are not made aware of informal, localised arrangements. Control is similarly threatened if managers themselves fail to put formal, written arrangements in place.

Benefits of formal health and safety arrangements

Safe working procedures do not happen by accident. Like quality control, they have to be planned. Every person's job description should outline the main areas of responsibility, duties and limits of authority. The inclusion of precise and minute details will be determined in the light of the competence of the individuals concerned, and of the risk levels involved.

Important advantages of this procedure

The written statement is a formal communication of health and safety duties from manager to subordinate. It can be questioned, explained and agreed through face-to-face discussion.

In this way, it is not taken for granted. Both parties can be assured that, at this stage, the maximum effort has been made to establish the individual's awareness and concern for health and safety. The written statement also:

- defines every employee's responsibility. Together, these descriptions provide the basis for the management control system, and for any employee to become aware of the duties and responsibilities of relevant colleagues
- minimises unnecessary duplication of duties or procedures, and decisions taken together should help to highlight areas or issues needing further attention
- can be revised or updated in the event of changes in staff, legislation, working practices, or for organisational reasons
- most importantly, for monitoring and controlling, can be used in measuring performance in achieving health and safety objectives.

The fact that this can be done, and is known to be done, should act as a positive motivator to employees at all levels to work to the required standards.

Performance standards

Performance standards have to be established for us to monitor and control health and safety. They will be determined after detailed analysis of the needs of the organisation and of predictable hazards and risks.

They should be devised for all work relevant to health and safety. This will include the work of managers at all levels and other employees. Performance standards should contain the following four elements.

Who is responsible? The standard should state the name and position of those responsible for carrying out the work. The necessary competence criteria for doing that work will also be specified.

What for? The standard will specify what has to be done, and how. This may involve outlining certain procedures or work systems, or use of special documents or equipment, for example:

- providing training to conform with PUWER before an employee can use certain equipment
- carrying out assessments under The Management Regulations before undertaking an operation involving significant risk
- checking the health and safety policy and records of contractors before awarding contracts.

When? Standards will specify when particular health and safety work is to take place. It may be on a regular basis, like a monthly inspection, or when a particular situation arises, such as the delivery of dangerous material.

With what results? The standard needs to state what is expected to be achieved by carrying out the particular health and safety activity. It could be expressed in terms of complying with a legal requirement. It may refer to the satisfactory completion of a training or inspection procedure.

Setting performance standards

Although we may believe that we are primarily concerned with health and safety management on site, the site does not exist in a vacuum. Hazards and risks can be brought onto a site. Equally, we can pass on risks to other people while our work is going on, or in the service or product we supply. The whole health and safety control system should include performance standards for all three stages: before, during and after the completion of the product or service.

Stage 1: Control of inputs

The objective is to eliminate and minimise hazards and risks on, or coming onto the site. We need performance standards to cover:

- **physical resources**, such as design and construction of workplaces, procurement of plant, materials and substances, including those used by contractors
- **personnel**, including the recruitment and selection of employees and selection of contractors
- **information**, for example, awareness and availability of technical and legal information relating to health and safety in the industry, and to general policies for risk control and for the development of a health and safety culture.

Stage 2: People and jobs

The objective is to eliminate or minimise risks arising from within the organisation, on site, where people work. Performance standards will cover these elements:

- **premises**, everything involved in the work environment
- **plant and substances**, including use, handling and storage
- **procedures**, the way work is done
- **people**, the effective matching of employees to tasks, including their competence and personal health issues.

Managers will not only consider performance standards affecting these four elements while the contract is following its normal course, but also in the following 'non-standard' circumstances:

- while maintenance or some other 'non-production' activity is taking place
- during planned changes in any of the four elements
- in the assessment of any foreseeable emergencies, guidance and the procedures for dealing with them
- during eventual completion, involving dismantling and removal of access and other facilities, plant and substances.

Stage 3: Control of outputs

The objective is to minimise risks to anybody who may be affected by the activities being undertaken. At this stage, performance standards are needed to cover potential health and safety issues such as:

- the design of fittings and systems in the building
- the materials used
- the installation and maintenance of systems
- off-site risks resulting from the work, including the emissions and disposal of waste materials
- the health and safety information for eventual users of the building or facility should be in the CDM health and safety file, including information covering, for example, heating, lighting, ventilation, air-conditioning, electronic control systems, electrical and other utilities installed.

In addition, the organisational structure which drives the health and safety policy needs its own performance standards. It must be sure that plans and standards are implemented; that effective communication of policy and plans takes place; that universal appreciation of risks and their control is continually improved.

Managers and supervisors do not operate in a vacuum within their organisations and, to ensure that the health and safety policy and arrangements are effective, there is a need to ensure that a positive 'health and safety culture' is in existence.

The four Cs of a positive health and safety culture are:

- **Competence**: recruitment, training and advisory support
- **Control**: allocating responsibilities and securing commitment
- **Co-operation**: between individuals and groups
- **Communication**: verbal, written and visible.

The principles outlined above are contained in the statutory requirements as set out in The Health and Safety at Work Act and associated health and safety legislation. The emphasis is on good management practice being applied, through an organisation's procedures, for the successful conduct of its business.

Reference
***HSE** publications*
***HSG65** Successful Health and Safety Management*
***HSG48** Reducing error and influencing behaviour*

Measuring, monitoring and auditing health and safety performance

Measuring health and safety performance

This section concerns the use that can be made of the statistics produced through the organisation's control procedures. The frequency of accidents and other events provides a means of measuring the health and safety performance of the organisation over a given time.

The results, compared with those of others, and with the organisation's earlier results, will help to identify any need for improving or modifying working methods.

Accident comparisons

Statistical evidence

Statistical comparisons of one group of workers against another, or comparison of group statistics from one year to another, presents many difficulties and can cause incorrect conclusions to be drawn. Notably, errors in interpretation could be made, because of changes that have occurred in the membership of groups from year to year, or just because the circumstances of two groups are so different that a useful comparison cannot be made.

The value of comparisons

Health and safety performance can be assessed by using the most recent results in several ways, by:

- relating them to the same period of the last year, quarter or month
- comparing them with those of other organisations engaged in similar contracts with similar risks
- comparing them with like or similar departments in your own organisation
- relating them to official national statistics for similar operations
- comparing results between work teams on the same site and on similar sites
- making regional comparisons between sites in different parts of the country.

In a climate of open communication between managers, such comparisons should be extremely fruitful in helping to identify and deal with problem areas. Exchange of ideas on hazard recognition and risk reduction can help to develop a positive health and safety environment.

Use of accident statistics

The most accurate figures available are the Health and Safety Statistics published in the supplements to the Annual Report of the Health and Safety Commission.

Statistical information, summarised from an employer's duty to report certain classes of accident under The Reporting of Injuries, Diseases and Dangerous Occurrences Regulations (RIDDOR) 1995, is collated by the Health and Safety Executive, and published in the Health and Safety Commission Annual Report. The validity of such data depends on employers complying fully with legal reporting requirements, and the figures have to be interpreted accordingly.

For many small organisations, reportable injuries represent a very small proportion of their total injuries to employees. It is known that statistics only have value if the data is large enough to be considered as typical. The use of major injury accident data, or over-three-day accident data, may not be truly realistic.

It is helpful, therefore, to make use of several indices for calculating incidence rates. In this way it is possible to monitor trends over periods of time and between different parts of the site or the whole of the organisation.

These calculations can be used for all accidents or events put together, or to isolate specific events such as injuries caused by falling from heights or using particular equipment; or ill health arising from the use of a particular substance.

*Calculations required for statistical purposes can be found in Construction Site Safety **(GE 700)**, Chapter A13 Accident reporting and investigation*

Adverse factors in construction

When comparing the building and civil engineering industry with other industries, especially those which are factory based, it is important to take into account the factors which adversely affect the accident rate in the building and civil engineering industry. These include the following:

- construction site work operations can change from day to day/hour by hour
- the labour force, including supervisors, may change frequently
- the size of the labour force may vary from day to day/week by week
- hazardous work situations exist, such as working at height, temporary platforms, excavations or in tunnels, etc.
- work involves exposure to the elements such as wind, rain, snow, cold, sun and heat, etc.
- new building products are frequently introduced.

Refer to RIDDOR for legal requirements on health and safety events that must be recorded and reported.

Reference
Construction Industry Advisory Committee Publication
Guidance on the Collection and Use of Accident Information in the Construction Industry

CITB-ConstructionSkills Publication
*Construction Site Safety **(GE 700)***
Chapter A01 Health and safety law
Chapter A10 Inspection and audits
Chapter A13 Accident reporting and investigation

Active monitoring

The purpose of active monitoring is to measure success in regular compliance with the standards of health and safety performance. Different levels of monitoring will obviously reflect the structure of the organisation, and a system of reporting will confirm that monitoring is taking place as planned.

Examples of some forms of active monitoring:

- managers check the quality of monitoring delegated to their subordinates
- the scrutiny of regular health and safety reports and returns at lower levels of management, including safety advisers
- the examination and review of health and safety documents in use
- the periodic review of health and safety training needs
- the systematic inspection of premises, plant and equipment
- environmental and health monitoring to detect early signs of damage to health
- the direct observation of working practices by first line supervisors
- the inclusion of regular health and safety reports at senior management level and board meetings.

Monitoring efforts should be targeted where they will produce the most benefit and lead to the greatest control of risks.

Regular and systematic monitoring can be supplemented by random or irregular events, such as unannounced spot-checks or site inspections by managers, safety representatives or hired-in consultants.

Any or all of these active monitoring procedures provide evidence to employees that management is genuinely committed to a safe and healthy working environment, as stated in the health and safety policy.

Reactive monitoring

Reactive systems monitor anything that has actually happened: accidents, incidents, near-misses and ill health. They require managers to recognise and report effectively on:

- the nature and cause of injuries and ill health
- events such as damage to physical resources
- any existing hazards
- the weaknesses or failures in compliance with health and safety performance standards
- near miss reporting – incidents where injury or loss of some kind was only narrowly avoided.

Major events are generally reported effectively. However, it is easy to overlook minor injuries and small events of loss or minor damage, because their implications appear minimal. This is potentially dangerous. Longer-term outcomes cannot be foreseen, and the seemingly trivial event of today may be the warning of a disaster waiting to happen.

The reporting of **all** events can be encouraged by:

- communication and training, so the reasons for reporting all events are made clear to everyone
- developing co-operative attitudes in the working culture, so that all employees become more observant and responsive – another benefit of open communication
- cross-checking through different documentation, such as maintenance reports and fire reports, to detect any events, or potential events, that would not have otherwise come to light.

Investigation and response systems for active and reactive monitoring

Systems are needed to ensure a consistent response to, and thorough investigation of, substandard performance.

The results of investigations also need to be analysed and reviewed so as to identify common features and trends that might reveal areas for general improvement. These systems must be operated by staff who have the necessary level of competence.

Inspection in active monitoring

The inspection of plant, facilities and working practices is essential for effective active monitoring. Tests, examinations and inspections are required by legislation and include such items as cranes and associated lifting gear, hoists, scaffolding and supports to excavations, trenches and shafts. However, a full inspection programme should cover all relevant performance standards.

Inspection schedules should be drawn up, with the frequency of inspection related to legal or operating requirements and to risk levels. Inspection forms and reports to provide feedback on compliance with standards and for later analysis and, if necessary, modifying action should support the procedure.

The types of inspection and monitoring systems can be found in *Construction Site Safety (GE 700), Chapter A10 Inspections and audits*.

Health and safety reports

Whatever else your organisation may specify, reports on accidents, ill health or other incidents including near-misses should contain the following basic essentials:

The event itself:

- the full personal details of employee(s) involved
- a description of the circumstances, including time, date and place and other relevant conditions
- full details of the event
- all events leading up to it
- any direct cause(s) of any loss, including injury
- the immediate cause(s) of the event
- any root (longer-term) cause(s), such as control failure, lack of competence, poor training, human issues
- details of the outcome, for example, injury to members of the public, damage to property, creation of new hazards and the severity of harm caused to people and physical resources
- any immediate response by management, including its promptness, quality of emergency procedures followed, first-aid response
- an assessment of whether and how the event could have been prevented.

Potential consequences:

- what was the worst that could have happened?
- how was that prevented?
- how often, or in what circumstances, could such an event reoccur?
- what could have been the most severe injury or damage to result from this event?
- how many people, employees or others, could have been affected by the event?

Responsibility

You must remember that you are responsible for the content of your report, regardless of how the information is provided or who supplied it. While receiving and accepting information at face value, you should be prepared to check its accuracy and validity.

However, you should approach this positively and constructively, not in a recriminatory ('deciding who is to blame') way. This will help to preserve the confidence your subordinates have in you, and to nurture the co-operation you all need to achieve health and safety objectives.

Health and safety auditing systems

Following effective planning, organisation and control, the continuing need for efficient monitoring is paramount in any organisation's systems.

The Approved Code of Practice (ACoP) for The Management Regulations, states that progressive improvement, in health and safety performance, 'can only be achieved through the constant development of policies, approaches to implementation and techniques of risk control'.

The use of an auditing system is one way of monitoring, in depth, the effectiveness of the performance standards and the implementation of those standards within an organisation.

The purpose of auditing

To audit is to make a searching examination. All control systems can stagnate or lose relevance due to changing conditions. Auditing can provide an assessment of the control system's effectiveness, independently of those responsible for its planning and operation.

A safety audit is a demonstration of the management's commitment to improve the overall safety of the workplace, rather than a straightforward fault-finding inspection. The aim of such an audit is to identify any problem areas that may exist in the organisation.

The audit should look at the interaction of all activities, as well as those activities themselves.

It must be in addition to the organisation's health and safety policy, in that it will help management to judge just how well health and safety is being managed.

By adopting safety auditing as the active approach to safety, the employer will be attempting to identify problems and possible causes of accidents before they happen. Once these are identified, the employer will be able to change working practices to minimise unsafe actions, thereby making a safer working environment.

A good audit will benefit everyone from senior management through to the employee, and will be accepted on its merits as the resultant changes bring improvements in health and safety performance.

For maximum benefit, competent people who are quite independent of the activity or policy being examined should handle the audit. External consultants may be involved here, although managers should be wary of using off-the-peg audit systems not developed for their organisation. CITB-ConstructionSkills' *Construction Site Safety – Health, Safety and Environmental Auditing System (SA 03CD)* should be considered as a first stage on the auditing ladder, with other more complex systems available as the size of the task becomes more involved.

The effective audit system

The audit system should be able to assess these key elements:

- the purpose, range and adequacy of the health and safety policy itself
- the organisation, including control arrangements, employee involvement and communication
- the planning and implementation of the health and safety policy, including management responsibilities, performance standards and compliance with them, resources and the long-term improvements in health and safety performance
- the effectiveness of measuring and review systems, and the ability to learn from them.

This last element is important: the audit system is only as good as those who operate it. Controls may have to be incorporated to guard against abuse of the audit procedures.

Most importantly, its value depends heavily on the quality and sensitivity of the responses, judgements and decisions made by managers on the basis of their audit findings. Such decisions must themselves become subject to later auditing and review.

Several safety auditing systems are available commercially. In the main these are directed at the larger organisations which can afford either to employ their own dedicated auditing team or contract consultants to come in and carry out the audit as impartial outsiders.

CITB-ConstructionSkills' publication *Construction Site Safety – Health, Safety and Environmental Auditing System (SA 03CD)* is closely related to *Construction Site Safety (GE 700)*, and is aimed at those organisations which are unable, or do not have the time, to organise or generate their own auditing system. It is the first step that the smaller- and medium-sized organisations will take on the road to full health and safety auditing.

The purpose of the audit system is to monitor an organisation's (or part of an organisation's) operations to evaluate their approach to health and safety, and to identify those areas which may need attention to improve health and safety. It is designed to be carried out on a regular basis, but within a time scale set by the organisation itself.

Summary

No audit, however good or thorough, is of any use unless it is backed up by feedback from both directions. A report containing information relating to the audit must be relayed from the auditor to the management. The auditor must notify any problems, and areas which need attention.

Audit reports must be short, concise, unambiguous and readable. Management must inform the auditor that they acknowledge the result of the audit and indicate what they intend to do to rectify any problems identified. It will not be necessary to advise of the completion of the rectified items, as this would be picked up at the next audit.

The object of the health and safety audit is to check whether an organisation as a whole, or just in part, is meeting the criteria which have been set for the standard of health and safety the organisation desires.

Mr Justice Fennell QC, when giving judgement at the enquiry following the King's Cross fire in 1987, stated that:

'Management will only receive the standard of safety that they demonstrate that they want.'

Information and training

The manager's information needs

The Health and Safety at Work Act imposes on employers the duty to provide the information necessary to ensure the health and safety at work of all employees. The Management Regulations makes this more specific by stating that every employer shall provide employees with relevant and easily understood information on:

- the risks to their health and safety identified by risk assessments
- the risks notified to the manager, by other employers, in shared workplaces
- the preventative and protective measures, in place, to minimise those risks
- the procedures for minimising serious and imminent danger.

Managers responsible for any aspect of health and safety management need good sources of information on subjects such as changing legislation, technical developments and new initiatives in health and safety practice. Information has three dimensions:

- it comes into the organisation from external sources, and is interpreted and acted upon
- as part of that process, information flows and circulates inside the organisation
- managers may also be responsible for conveying information to agencies, authorities or individuals outside their own organisation.

Much of the information received from external sources is interpreted by managers, and conveyed to employees within the organisation.

Managers are responsible for ensuring that the information received and put into circulation is easily understood and up to date. They should be familiar with the range of material available from such sources, as they will have to assess the information needs of their employees and the best means of meeting them.

Major external information sources

Advisory material is issued by such bodies as:

- Health and Safety Commission
- Health and Safety Executive
- British Standards Institution
- Royal Society for the Prevention of Accidents
- Construction Confederation
- CITB-ConstructionSkills.

Material published by such organisations can form the basis of sound health and safety practice. Employees can be reassured by the fact that their employer takes seriously the guidance provided by these authoritative and independent sources.

Individual organisations will decide how much of this material to make available in its original state. The Health and Safety Executive has prepared guidance on the implementation of legislation.

In addition, they have produced a number of leaflets that provide a basic understanding of health and safety matters and are easily understood.

Approved Codes of Practice (ACoPs)

In line with the provisions of The Health and Safety at Work Act, regulations are being produced to supersede previous health and safety legislation, along with Approved Codes of Practice (ACoPs). These give guidance on the implementation of those regulations in easily understandable language rather than the formal language of legislation. The Health and Safety Commission has the power to approve and issue Codes of Practice. It can also approve codes issued by other bodies and industry advisory bodies, such as the British Standards Institution.

The information contained in the ACoPs should assist managers and supervisors to identify and fulfil their obligations under both current and new legislation.

Special status of ACoPs

The special status of an ACoP is confirmed by The Health and Safety at Work Act.

Whilst failing to comply with an Approved Code of Practice is not an offence, the failure could be used as evidence of a breach of legislation. An organisation would need to satisfy the court that it had complied with the regulations in some other way.

Guidance notes

Guidance Notes, issued by the HSE, do not have a legal status, however prosecutors may use them in court to support a case.

Guidance for the industry from particular advisory committees may be issued. They carry only the limited authority of the committee concerned. The Construction Industry Advisory Committee (CONIAC) is an example.

Guidance notes from industry frequently come from manufacturers and similar associations. They focus on practical instructions for particular conditions and workplaces. While the HSC and HSE welcome this valuable guidance, they do not normally give such publications their official recognition.

Under this heading, we should include the quite specific and detailed operating instructions provided by suppliers or manufacturers of tools, equipment and materials.

Information for employees

Effective communication within an organisation is vital to achieve proper understanding and implementation of the health and safety policy.

Whatever the content or purpose of the communication, managers and supervisors have to consider:

- the most suitable means of conveying the information
- the levels of training, knowledge and experience of employees receiving it.

In addition to using techniques within the three broad communication methods, consideration is needed for those with language difficulties or reading problems, as well as for employees whose first language is not English. In such cases, interpreters or translators may be needed and greater use should be made of visual communication, such as symbols or diagrams, than of the written word.

The emphasis on co-operation and open communication is directly applicable here.

If a co-operative culture is established, communication of all kinds will be more effective. This will lead to health and safety policy and practices being properly understood, accepted and put into effect.

In general, information and guidance on real or potential hazards and any other health, safety or welfare issues will be provided to all employees likely to be affected by them.

Employees exposed to health risks

In the case of specific health hazards, employees must be informed of the nature of the risks and the preventative and protective measures to be taken, including any they should take to safeguard themselves. They must receive full details of the results of relevant monitoring checks. Where potential health hazards are very dangerous, detailed notification must be given in writing to any affected employee, identified by name. Employees should formally sign that they have received such information, and that they agree to observe the stated precautions, and are willing to undergo any necessary medical tests connected with the hazard.

Information on new equipment, substances and processes

Periodically, operatives may encounter unfamiliar working conditions. For example, they may move to a site using much larger industrial plant than they are used to, along with new technology or newly developed materials or adhesives. In such events employees must be trained, and supervised if necessary, in the new techniques of operation, handling, storage or erection required. There is a particular danger when the new feature resembles the old, as formerly acceptable practices will have to be 'unlearned' and replaced by new ones.

Effective flow of information

All affected employees, as well as those with specific duties, need to know:

- the health and safety responsibilities of each person concerned
- the established lines of communication for health and safety matters
- the nature of the information that individuals require
- which individuals require that information
- the most suitable form(s) in which to make that information available
- the precise location of the individuals concerned, and how and when they can be contacted.

Information leaving the organisation

Health and safety information is required by various agencies or bodies outside the organisation. Fatal and major injuries to employees, self-employed people and members of the public, and over three-day injuries, must be reported to the HSE or the local authority as appropriate, under RIDDOR. The Health and Safety at Work Act requires information to be provided about the safe use of articles and substances within the workplace.

For a variety of reasons, it may be necessary to communicate with planning authorities, emergency services and local residents. These groups must be involved in emergency planning where The Control of Major Accident Hazards Regulations (COMAH) 2005 apply.

Communication of the relevant information in these areas may be supplemented by the use of local press or broadcast media. Once again, information must be presented in suitable forms that can be readily understood by those receiving it. Professional advice may be needed in difficult situations. The effectiveness of communication systems will be crucial in emergency conditions, and may well require special contingency arrangements to be put in place.

Training for health and safety

Introduction

The Health and Safety at Work Act and The Management Regulations impose a duty on employers to train their employees in order to improve their capabilities and training in terms of health and safety at work.

In particular The Management Regulations require employers to:

- take into account employees' capabilities as regards health and safety when entrusting tasks to them
- ensure that employees are given adequate health and safety training:
  a) on being recruited – induction
  b) on being exposed to a new or increased risk through transfer or change of responsibilities, new equipment, new technology, or new work systems
  c) in the form of repeat training where appropriate, to adapt it in response to changing health and safety risks, and to provide it during working hours.

These requirements emphasise a central feature of training in general. It is a vehicle for change in individual employees, a response to change in the overall working environment and ensures compliance with legislation.

Training and recruitment

The competence of employees at every level has to be ensured if they are to make the best contribution to health and safety. Recruitment procedures will clearly be designed to select those with the physical and mental abilities necessary for their jobs. However, new employees, and especially young workers, will have particular training needs.

New employees should receive basic induction training on health and safety. Future training needs can be identified at this stage by:

- checking the new employee's qualifications, experience and training already received
- incorporating specific training determined by risk assessment procedures
- ongoing responses to changing conditions in the work environment.

Training and change

Any change in an employee's working environment could cause them to be exposed to a new or increased risk and therefore further training may be needed. Examples of change could be:

- an employee transferred to new work, or given new responsibilities. The changed nature or location of the work could contain hazards not previously experienced or covered in earlier training
- a significant change in equipment or working methods that will lead to a need for a review and reassessment of risks. The outcome of such a review may highlight additional training needs
- radical change such as completely new technology which may embody unfamiliar risks. Specialist training provided from outside the organisation could be required.

Refresher training

If skills are not used regularly, competence declines. To prevent this, training has to be repeated and extended periodically. Simple examples are regular fire or other emergency drills.

Analysis of health and safety checks, and accident or incident investigations, will alert managers to retraining needs. Employees who deputise for others with specific health and safety duties, should be remembered when refresher training is being considered. Employees returning from long absence due to illness or injury should also be reviewed for retraining.

The health and safety training cycle

Introduction

We can now look at a typical training procedure to guide managers and supervisors involved in planning and conducting health and safety training programmes.

The overall aim of such programmes is to help employees, at all levels, to acquire or develop the knowledge, skills and attitudes to make them competent in the health and safety aspects of their work. Training will be supported by appropriate supervision, sometimes close or continuous in particular circumstances, for example, young or inexperienced workers.

The background to the training cycle is the organisation's health and safety policy document, and job specifications incorporating health and safety requirements.

The cycle has six phases:

Deciding if training is needed

This decision is taken by using the combined information from job specifications and the known abilities, experience and previous training of individuals. This data is compared with what we want people to know and to be able to do in health and safety terms. Any variation between the two reveals a potential training requirement.

Identifying training needs

This takes us closer to finding out who should be trained and what they should be taught. People's jobs can be analysed from the health and safety point of view as follows:

- look at accident and health records related to those jobs to determine causes and preventative means
- discussions with employees about their working procedures, sequencing, tools, equipment and materials used
- observing and questioning employees about their methods and procedures.

This kind of analysis may be applied to a whole job, or to individual tasks. In this way, managers can target individual employees and their personal training needs. Regular performance appraisals can also identify training needs in the individual, especially where changes of role, responsibility or other factors in the work environment are involved.

Training needs also arise at the organisational level. They may include development of positive attitudes towards the health and safety culture, or the communication of new regulations or procedures within the organisation.

Managers and supervisors with specific health and safety duties may require training themselves in related areas, such as: leadership or communication skills; techniques of health and safety management; interpretation and implementation of new regulations, operating review and audit systems.

Identifying objectives

Here we clarify what we want the targeted employees to learn through their training. Priorities can be determined in the light of timing and relative risks. For example, early instruction in the safe handling, storage and use of some hazardous materials is essential if the material is arriving on the site in three days' time.

Learning objectives, if accurately and precisely stated, can become the basis for the later evaluation of the training programme's effectiveness.

Deciding on training methods

According to the expertise available, training may be conducted within the organisation or by using external trainers. At task level, a good deal of training takes place through coaching by supervisors or experienced operatives.

Trainers and demonstrators used in this way must be appropriately qualified and competent.

Training methods chosen should encourage the fullest participation by trainees. Indeed, their involvement in all phases of the cycle is a positive motivator. If employees have been able to contribute to setting up and evaluating the training programme, they will appreciate the need for it, and will identify with it and its success.

Carrying out the training

On-the-job training can itself generate new risks, and some training may have to be done elsewhere, using simulated conditions. Equally, the industry can make considerable use of specialist health and safety professionals.

Courses may be run by educational establishments, employer associations or trade unions. Suppliers of special equipment will often train their customers themselves. The emergency services, environmental health officers and government departments may all be able to contribute to specific training.

Faced with designing health and safety training programmes, managers need to become familiar with the range and variety of courses available.

Evaluating the training given

Training must be evaluated to determine that it has achieved its objectives. Managers and supervisors should satisfy themselves that:

- practical responses to health and safety issues have improved following specific training
- the training has been worth the money spent on it.

The training plan, structure, content, and methods may be subject to revision following evaluation – allowing it to respond to a changing work environment.

Promoting health and safety training

Health and safety training is sometimes viewed with suspicion, and those who are targeted may feel they are being picked on, or that their performance is thought to be sub-standard. Incentives such as promotion or increased pay, applicable to some forms of training, do not generally result from health and safety training.

Managers must encourage their employees to engage willingly and positively in such training. The task can be even more difficult in organisations with limited training history. The following points will help in this important initial stage:

- as indicated, encourage employees' genuine participation in the development of their training programmes
- raise their awareness of the responsibilities of both employers and employees. For health and safety, these are covered by existing legislation and ACoPs
- use relevant examples from your own sector of the industry to illustrate the consequences of inadequate health and safety training
- inform employees about the organisation's training policy, including how individuals are chosen for training. Also provide practical arrangements about payment of wages or salaries during training or reimbursements of expenses or fees paid
- help employees to become more aware of the considerable variety of training provision available, some of which they may be able to pursue on their own through open learning systems
- support and reassure those who may lack confidence when embarking on a formal course for the first time since leaving school
- at every stage of your involvement with potential trainees, emphasise the value to everyone concerned of the short- and long-term benefits of a working life free from injury and ill health.

Conclusion

The establishment of training needs and objectives provides managers with the raw material to produce detailed training programmes for both individuals and groups of employees at every level. They will address short-, medium- and long-term requirements, and allow for necessary refresher training. Programmes should be flexible so that they can be adapted in response to both predicted and unexpected changes.

Increased activity in health and safety training means increased paperwork. It is important that the employer maintains detailed records of all such training. Apart from its obvious practical value, this documentation confirms the organisation's commitment to the realities of its health and safety policy statement. It also provides essential evidence of its compliance with the provisions of the relevant legislation.

Advice on the full range of health and safety training in the construction industry can be obtained from the Company Development Advisers attached to a number of CITB-ConstructionSkills' offices.

Full information on the activities of CITB-ConstructionSkills can be found on the CITB-ConstructionSkills website and in Construction Site Safety ***(GE 700)*** *Introduction.*

Control of hazards and risks

General principles

Introduction

The effective control of hazards and risks lies at the heart of successful planning for health and safety. Earlier sections of this guidance contain advice on planning, monitoring, controlling and performance standards.

This part of the guidance draws this advice together, and develops it in dealing with the stages of risk control needed to comply with The Health and Safety at Work Act, The Management Regulations, and other applicable legislation.

The HSE's publication *HSG65 Successful Health and Safety Management*, the practical guide for managers and inspectors on health and safety management, provides a framework. We also draw on the ACoP for The Management Regulations.

Construction specific legislation places duties not only on employers, contractors and the self-employed, but also on clients, co-ordinators, designers and principal contractors. These set out the principles of prevention and protection required to be put into practice by managers and supervisors in their management of health and safety on site.

*Further information can be found in Construction Site Safety **(GE 700)**, Chapter A05 Risk assessments and method statements*

General principles of prevention and protection

These principles are seen as fundamental, and must be applied, to risk control planning.

- **If possible, avoid the risk completely**, by using different materials or methods if they are not essential to the activity.
- **Combat risks at source**, rather than simply providing warnings about potential risks.
- **Wherever possible, adapt work to the individual**, especially in choice of workplace, equipment and methods of working.
- **Take advantage of technological progress** that can make work safer and more efficient.
- **Give priority to measures protecting the whole work environment**, to produce the greatest benefit for all involved, rather than the individual.
- **An active health and safety culture must exist**, therefore the principles of risk prevention and protection should be part of everyone's attitude, at every level, in every activity.
- **Incorporate preventive measures in a coherent policy** so as to progressively reduce or eliminate risks.

The stages of risk control

These stages provide the planning structure for hazard and risk control:

- **PLAN – hazard identification** – identify potential sources of hazard
- **ORGANISE – risk assessment** – assess risks arising from identified hazards.

Remove the risk if you can

- **CONTROL – risk control** – decide on measures to control or eliminate risks
- **MONITOR – implement and maintain controls** – put controls into practice and monitor their effectiveness.

Then look at how you did

- **REVIEW – suitable and sufficient risk assessment** – review and edit regularly to ensure it remains fit for purpose.

Write it down

PLAN – hazard identification

Introduction

This first essential step requires a thorough understanding of the working environment. Individuals at every level who can make a useful contribution should be encouraged. In extremely complex or high risk situations, specialist advice and analysis techniques may be necessary.

Adequate information is essential, and the following should be considered:

- existing legislation and supporting ACoPs
- HSE publications and other guidance available
- product information (The Health and Safety at Work Act)
- British, European and International standards
- guidance from industry or trade associations
- knowledge and experience of managers, supervisors and employees
- health and safety reports and statistics, from both internal and external sources
- specialist advice and opinion.

Successful control demands a systematic hazard identification in these four main areas:

- human factors, for example, new or inexperienced employees, young persons
- the physical environment, for example, hot or cold, wet and windy weather
- plant, tools and equipment, for example, heavy or unwieldy plant, electrical tools
- working methods, for example, confined spaces, at height.

Human factors

The Health and Safety at Work Act and The Management Regulations impose a duty on employers to provide their employees with proper and adequate information, instruction, training and supervision. This will include identifying hazards and knowing the necessary action to take to eliminate or reduce the associated risks.

The individual's effectiveness in that respect depends partly on the general culture of the workplace and partly on the employees' own attitudes, motivation and sense of responsibility. The development of those personal factors may have to form part of the manager's task in protecting health and safety standards.

Employees also bring potential hazards with them, in the form of physical or intellectual weaknesses, along with social or domestic problems. Clearly, anyone with an identified medical condition must not work in positions or with any process or substances that could harm them further, or cause them to harm others.

The manager and supervisor should be alert to any evidence of impaired health or physical disability, or to the abuse of drugs or alcohol. Jobs can be redesigned, or special equipment provided, to compensate for the effects of some disablements, but some other problems, such as a fear of heights, have more obvious common-sense solutions.

*A fuller description of the effects of human factors on health and safety at work, can be found in the Health and Safety Executive publication **HSG48** Reducing error and influencing behaviour and Construction Site Safety **(GE 700)** Chapter A08 Behavioural safety*

The physical environment

The nature of the workplace can change very quickly and dramatically. Two days of continuous rain, at an early stage in the project, will convert a previously stable environment into a quagmire with its own new inherent hazards. On a large site, there may be deep excavations and a constant movement of people, heavy plant and vehicles. Innumerable other hazards can arise from work that is already in progress, such as loose or badly stacked materials, debris, uneven and unfinished floors, noise, dust, poor ventilation, noxious chemicals and electric cables.

Plant, tools and equipment

Items of plant, tools and equipment are specifically covered by legislation and identified within PUWER.

Managers and supervisors are responsible for ensuring that these are regularly maintained, inspected and tested but, in themselves, they contain potential risks, from design faults to wear and tear. They are also subject to operative error or misuse. Operatives themselves can readily recognise hazards in items they frequently use and should draw attention to anything they are not prepared to use on safety grounds.

Working methods

Many working methods within the building and civil engineering industry are traditional, widely used and accepted, but their repeated effective use may conceal the existence of inherent hazards.

Managers and supervisors need to check:

- where a safe working method has been established, that the method is being followed in practice
- where no such procedure exists, that the work activity is analysed and a safe method produced and communicated fully to the operatives concerned
- where a change to machinery, material or working practice takes place, that a new safe method of working is established.

Identifying hazards

The five procedures listed below can be used to suit any work environment. They should involve the workforce and managers, and should contribute towards a systematic approach to hazard detection. This is an important means by which the organisation can communicate its commitment to its own health and safety policy to all its employees.

1. **Safety sampling.** A 10 to 15 minute unannounced tour of a selected workplace to note any faults and defects observed, and to identify good practice or otherwise. Comparison with the findings of previous sampling tours will provide some useful measurement of the effectiveness of health and safety management in that area.
2. **Safety tour.** An unannounced workplace visit by managers to achieve similar purposes. This provides for particularly realistic evaluation of the observance of preventative and protective measures, and of the quality of first-line supervisors in health and safety terms.
3. **Safety inspection.** A routine, scheduled inspection, to examine closely all health and safety arrangements for a particular work area. It includes the scrutiny of working methods as well as those of mandatory registers and other records. In this way, performance can be related to the organisation's standards and policy.
4. **Safety survey.** This is the 'vertical' approach to safety auditing. It will focus in great detail on a specific work activity, such as the erection and use of hoist towers, or excavation supports and guards, to confirm good safety practice and to highlight any weakness requiring remedial action.
5. **Safety auditing.** This is the 'horizontal' approach where scrutiny is made of part, or the whole, of the organisation's health and safety policy cycle. It may analyse and evaluate any aspect of the development of the policy itself, or of its organisation, planning, implementation, measurement and review.

Where the company has a safety adviser, they should be available for site visits in the event of pre-arranged or unannounced HSE inspections, or to respond to special requests from site managers to investigate accidents and dangerous occurrences. The safety adviser should prepare written reports confirming their findings and, where appropriate, recommendations on the remedial action to be taken. Such reports should be made available to the management, to conform with the company communication structure.

Hazard inspection reporting

As part of the overall communication structure, procedures should exist to report the findings of hazard inspections. Oral reporting to site management is important if remedial action is required urgently, followed by a report in writing – one copy to the site manager and one to the contracts manager, or project manager.

The report's initiator should request that the recipient confirms, within a specified time period, that any recommended remedial action has been taken. If not, the report should be sent to a higher managerial level for action.

On the next inspection visit, the person inspecting should check that remedial actions have been taken for those problems found at the last inspection.

ORGANISE – risk assessment

Introduction

In the context of the The Management Regulations, the term 'risk' expresses the likelihood that the harm from a particular hazard may be realised, and its extent 'covers the population which might be affected by a risk'.

The exposure of employees to risks in the workplace is inevitable, considering the nature of the work, the type of plant or equipment used, and the very nature of human beings and their responses to differing work situations and environments. However, it is the responsibility of the employer to remove the risk or reduce it to acceptable levels.

Priority is generally given to risks presenting the greatest severity. Where two risks are judged to produce similar consequences, priority treatment goes to the one most likely to occur.

Risk assessments are required by many regulations in addition to The Management Regulations. For example: The COSHH Regulations, The Control of Asbestos Regulations 2006 and The Control of Lead at Work Regulations 2002.

Where this kind of identifiable legal framework does not exist, those responsible for their employees' health and safety need to develop risk assessment techniques for themselves, to comply with the demands of the legislation. This requires thorough knowledge of all work activities, and contributions should be made by all those involved, be they managers, supervisors, other employees, safety representatives or safety advisers.

Three key definitions need to be understood:

- **Hazard** is something with the potential to cause harm
- **Risk** is the likelihood that the harm from the hazard is realised
- **Consequence** is the number of persons exposed to the risk.

Risk, therefore, represents both the likelihood of harm and the severity of the harm resulting from an uncontrolled risk.

A simple risk estimation

Every organisation will devise systems to suit its own needs. The following outline illustrates the general principles that should support those systems.

The effects of hazards can be rated in this way:

3 Major: death or possible major injury

2 Serious: off work for more than three days

1 Slight: all other injuries.

Harm may not result from being exposed to a hazard in every case. The likelihood is determined by the way work is organised, the effectiveness of any controls, the extent and nature of the exposure, and the experience of employees working with that hazard.

Likelihood of harm can be rated in this way:

3 High: certain or near certain harm

2 Medium: harm occurring frequently

1 Low: harm seldom occurring.

A risk is the combination of these two factors and can be expressed by multiplying them together. Thus, a risk of major severity 3 with a medium likelihood of occurring 2 is given risk rating 6. This figure enables different risks to be compared and could be multiplied further to reflect different sizes of population affected.

Priorities in other areas can also be based on risk assessments, such as deciding health and safety policy objectives, training and competence levels, the speed of response and the action to be taken following an injury or discovery of a hazard.

Guidelines to practical assessment

Introduction

The most important elements of risk assessment are that they must be suitable and sufficient, deal with likelihood and severity and cover all those involved in, or affected by, the activity being assessed.

In the simplest terms, a risk assessment starts with these questions:

- **What** is to be done? Consider plant or equipment, materials, people and environment.
- **How** is the operation or work to be done? Consider plant or equipment, people, materials and their environments.
- **Where** is it to be done? Consider how this affects plant or equipment, people, materials and environment.

It continues with the process of:

- identifying the significant hazards in the above areas
- determining the likelihood of injury or harm arising from the interaction of the above factors
- quantifying the severity and the consequences of the injury or harm to and from plant or equipment, people and materials
- identifying any specific legal requirements involving the interaction of the above factors
- developing the control measures to be implemented to remove or minimise the risk to or from people, plant or equipment and materials
- including information on the control, monitoring and review of the risk assessment
- including the provision of information to all those who may be affected by the operation both within and outside the workplace.

The purpose of a risk assessment is to try to prevent accidents and protect the health and safety of all employees, and others who may be affected by the work operation. It is important that the outcome of any risk assessment is a clear **method statement**. This should provide a safe system of work, a safe place of work and adequate protection to all who may be affected. The method statement must be clearly and simply communicated and must be understood by the employees carrying out the task. The statement should be in the form of **job safety instructions**. An obsession with a systems or procedures approach is to lose sight of the object of the assessment, which is to achieve high standards of prevention and protection of the health and safety for all.

A competent person is required to carry out a risk assessment or review an assessment. The level of competency required will depend on the complexity and technicality of the task in hand. Therefore, those assigned to the task, at whatever level of management, must have a combination of knowledge (of the task), skills (deductive), experience (in the field under review) and personal qualities (of management).

The HSE has produced some simple guidance for commercial, service and light industries. Individual companies have developed their own systems for undertaking risk assessments.

The questions below constitute a simple approach:

- What is the activity?
- How is the activity carried out?
- Where is it to be carried out? The ‘environment’?
- What people, plant, equipment, or materials are to be used?
- How are the hazards to be identified?
- By whom or at what level are risk assessments to be undertaken?
- How will a description of control measures be notified to those at risk?
- What type and level of communication will be undertaken?
- What training, instruction and supervision will need to be undertaken by the workforce?

Below are the prime considerations in the preparation of risk assessments.

- **Ensure all relevant risks are addressed.** Avoid giving a disproportionate amount of attention to trivial risks. Check that where a risk is partly controlled by some other means the remainder of the risk is properly assessed. Look at all aspects of the work activity and assess systematically.
- **Address what happens.** Actual practice may differ from an established working method. Include non-routine events, such as maintenance, events connected with vehicle use, changes in processes or work cycles.
- **Consider all groups of employees and others.** For example, maintenance staff, security guards, visitors to the site and various support workers such as office staff and caterers.
- **Identify employee groups particularly at risk.** These must include young workers, trainees, lone workers and those with disabilities.
- **Evaluate existing protective and preventive measures.** See that they are working properly. If they are, they may already be sufficient to cover all your statutory obligations. If not, they will require remedial action.

Where risk assessments have been conducted in response to other regulations, such as COSHH, new assessments are not required under The Management Regulations provided that they are still valid, and that all significant risks have been covered. Where a work situation is being assessed for the first time, a rough assessment could first be used to identify any aspects needing a detailed assessment under other regulations. The final assessment for The Management Regulations could then consist of those detailed assessments, plus aspects not covered elsewhere.

Once a conclusion has been reached on the best practical means of eliminating or reducing the risk to employees, the resulting control measures must be implemented in such a way that the activity can be carried out safely.

The means of implementation will be in the form of method statements, safe systems of work and direct instructions to the workforce in the form of job safety instructions.

Remove the risk if you can

CONTROL – risk control

Introduction

Risk control measures are only as good as the information provided by hazard identification and risk assessments. Some of the protective duties under The Health and Safety at Work Act and other legislation must be complied with absolutely. Many of them are qualified by other terms, for example, ‘so far as is reasonably practicable’ or ‘best practicable means’.

Preferred hierarchy of control principles

The manager’s decisions about priorities can be guided by the preferred hierarchy of risk control principles.

- **Design suitable systems of working.**
- **Combat risk at source.** For example, by completely enclosing a process, machine guarding or using remotely operated equipment.
- **Substitute the dangerous with the less dangerous.** Use a less hazardous substance, a better guarded machine or a safer process.
- **Use of personal protective equipment only as a last resort.**

The fact that the final item appears last, suggests that control measures which rely solely on people are regarded as the least effective.

Risk decisions must consider the degree of control needed and the reliability of the control measures to be implemented, as much as the costs of providing them. Control measures must satisfy the needs of all three elements involved in the work situation:

- the output needs of the organisation
- the quality needs of the job
- the health and safety needs of the people themselves.

Control of health risks

While the principles are the same for controlling risks to safety or risks to health, there are features of risks to health that require particular attention.

- Ill health often results from complex biological processes caused by, for example, noise levels or dust inhalation.
- With those processes which are longer-term, people may be at risk long before the hazard has been recognised and properly identified.
- Some diseases could have their cause outside the workplace as well as within it.
- Some diseases are not readily detectable until long or intense exposure to the risk has already taken place.

The implications for health risk assessment and control are these:

- health risk assessments will demand greater use of internal or external specialist expertise than is needed for many safety risks
- competent measuring and monitoring of exposure is required
- measurement of working environments is needed to ensure that any physical control systems installed are operating within their required limits.

The outcome of a risk assessment should be used as the basis of a **method statement**. This statement is the means by which the control measures are communicated to employees.

The statement should cover the following items:

- what is to be done
- how it is to be done
- the identity of person(s) with special responsibilities
- the identity of hazards and specific precautions to be taken
- the personal protective equipment to be used (if required in addition to the specific precautions to be taken)
- emergency procedures
- means of communication.

If necessary, the method statement should be broken down into **job safety instructions** for individual employees. The simple clear statements of each step of the work to be carried out and the safe method of work to be used. The job safety instructions can also be used in identifying training needs.

MONITOR – implementing risk controls

Introduction

It may take time to implement some controls fully but, at any stage where complete control cannot be achieved, interim measures are needed to minimise risks. Implementation may involve some training sessions, but the risks do not disappear during the training period.

Maintaining risk controls

Risk controls must contain their own systems for monitoring and review and the frequency of inspection and review will reflect the relative importance of the risks concerned. As already indicated, working conditions can change rapidly, so this factor will also influence the frequency of maintenance activities.

Well-designed risk controls only have value if the people affected by the risks observe the rules and carry out the procedures. Success here relies on the quality of the organisation's communications system and techniques.

The notion of 'reward' may also be considered. Monitoring activities such as safety tours or inspections should openly highlight the good practices observed, as well as detecting and correcting sub-standard performance.

REVIEW – suitable and sufficient assessments

This expression is contained in The Management Regulations. It is not further defined, and so provides flexibility for the relative evaluation of assessments, which must account for the complex nature of the work activity, the nature and effects of the materials used, the effects of the environment and the individual human nature that employees bring to the workplace.

This means that the suitability of a risk assessment can only be determined by relating it to the nature and degree of the risk involved. So suitable and sufficient risk assessments for one person undertaking the replacement of a roof on a house would be much more straightforward than for a large multi-million pound river crossing project.

Where unfamiliar risks or very complex processes are involved, specialist advice would have to be sought to ensure a suitable and sufficient assessment.

Construction sites have a particularly dynamic work environment. Work activities and the nature of the workplace itself change and develop frequently, and groups of operatives may move from one part of the site to another, or from site to site. Risk assessment here may have to concentrate on the broad range of risks arising, so that planning and training can take account of all the above factors and enable risks to be controlled should they arise.

The changing nature of construction work emphasises the need for constant review and revision. Risk assessment is not done once and for all because, as conditions change, so do the hazards and risks. It should become standard management practice to review and modify any risk assessment in line with the degree and frequency of changes known to be taking place.

Write it down

Record the findings

Employers with five or more employees must record the significant findings of their risk assessments in writing or electronically, provided that the electronic record can be retrieved for use by managers, examined by safety representatives or other inspectors.

The record should be an effective statement of identified hazards and their risks, which leads management to take the appropriate protective measures. It should be linked to other health and safety records that are required by The Health and Safety at Work Act and other legislation.

Significant findings should include:

- any hazards which would pose serious risks to workers, and others affected, if not properly controlled
- any existing control measures and an evaluation of their effectiveness
- persons affected by those risks, including any especially vulnerable groups of employees.

Records should be sufficiently detailed to show that the assessments undertaken are indeed 'suitable and sufficient', and can be properly reviewed and modified as necessary.

The ACoP for The Management Regulations states that a record is totally unnecessary only when, in the most straightforward and obvious cases, a risk assessment can be easily repeated and explained.

It should be emphasised that all parties to a construction project have obligations for hazard identification, and risk assessment, in contributing to the overall health and safety plan. As mentioned earlier, construction legislation imposes duties on clients, designers, co-ordinators, principal contractors, contractors, including employees and the self-employed.

From the above it can be seen that no one person, except in the case of very simple activities, can have all the attributes necessary to carry out the risk assessment. To achieve the best result and protect the workforce and workplace, it is essential that a '**team**' approach is adopted when carrying out the process.

Depending on the complexity of the work process, the skills necessary will include:

- a person or persons with knowledge of the work process. This may include design staff, operational management staff, maintenance personnel, etc.
- a person who has knowledge of the health and safety requirements and best practice
- a person representing the employees.

Each specialist within the work area can contribute considerable experience and knowledge, having the operational experience in carrying out the actual operation or activity.

Recording control measures

Some sets of regulations, COSHH being one example, include specific requirements for recording both assessments and control measures. The Management Regulations also contain such a requirement, in that employers should record all their health and safety arrangements: planning, organisation, control, monitoring and review. These arrangements should include a list of the 'competent persons' the employer has appointed to undertake the control measures.

This record could form part of the health and safety policy document which is required by The Health and Safety at Work Act.

The detail needed will reflect the degree of risk. The greater the risk, the greater the detail required. Everyday minor risks affecting all employees can be covered by simple rules, but more specific and complex risks will have detailed performance standards and procedures to be followed.

Notes

Notes